Advance Praise for *21 Days to Emotional Literacy*

"I had never heard of Emotional Literacy before working with Dan and Lucy. Now I see it as fundamental to understanding myself, my family, and my co-workers. Learning to name my emotions has helped bring clarity to my thinking."

—Suzanne J., Administrator, U.S.

"For me, completing this workbook was a very personal journey. I am a design engineer and I learned that emotions are at the center of all my choices, which surprised me. I feel much more calm and at ease learning about emotions in this way."

—Antonio D., Engineer, Italy

"Thinking about emotions having a time orientation is new to me, but made me realize how much some people live in the past and others live mostly in the future. That gives emotions a new dimension for me when I listen to people on my team."

—Agnes C., Marketing Manager, France

"I found it very easy to understand the idea that building emotional literacy starts with (1) listening to our emotions without judgment, (2) reflecting on what they are trying to tell us, and (3) articulating them in our own way. The more we do this, the more fluent we will become. I use it with my coachees every day!"

—Bill F., Executive Coach, Canada

"It took me three months, but when I finished the workbook, I realized that my understanding of emotions had really changed. I was always uncomfortable even admitting I had emotions, but now see them as normal (almost)."

—Alexi K., Business Leader, Russia

"At first I thought the exercises looked easy and would be quick to complete, but found that it was much harder than I expected. Just naming my emotions took a lot of time and reflection because it is something I never do. I'm happy I did the work, and my wife tells me it has made a big difference."

—Thomas K., Retired Accountant, U.S.

21 DAYS TO EMOTIONAL LITERACY

A PERSONAL STEP-BY-STEP WORKBOOK

DAN NEWBY AND LUCY NÚÑEZ

CALL TO ACTION

There are many avenues you can take to develop your Emotional Literacy. One is our book, **"The Unopened Gift: A Primer in Emotional Literacy,"** which articulates a new interpretation of emotions and their role in human life. It is a clear and complete presentation of Emotional Literacy, available on Amazon and Kindle in English and Spanish. Another is by taking our online programs, **"Emotions and Coaching"** and **"Emotions and Leadership,"** available at www.studyemotions.com. For other publications, tools, and live workshops or mentoring, please write to us at dan@dannewby.me or review our website www.dannewby.me. Please let us know how we can support your learning in the critical area of emotions.

DEDICATION

This book is dedicated to our many students throughout the world.
It is their interest and requests that have led to this workbook.
It is a great pleasure for us to be in contact with such passionate learners.

TABLE OF CONTENTS

PREFACE

Growing up, I can recall a lot of attention by parents, teachers, and peers on the question of intelligence. In school, many of us were sorted into groups based on cognitive testing and put into "tracks" that led to either college or technical school. Knowing one's IQ was a double-edged sword and could be either a source of inspiration and pride or of doubt about our ability to "live up to it." "Being smart" mattered.

With all the attention focused on intellect, we almost universally neglected another center of intelligence and source of wisdom, our emotions. Emotions were considered "in the way" of clear decision-making and it was believed to be beneficial if we could "set them aside" and rely on reason and logic alone. For a long time, humans have, in general, regarded emotions as a problem to be controlled or managed.

But there is another possibility. Maybe emotions exist for a reason; maybe they are there to help us. Since they are an undeniable part of our experience as human beings, how else could we understand and relate to them than the way we have?

If you are reading this workbook, it is likely that you have already come to the realization that it might be valuable to develop your emotional intelligence and are looking for a way to do that.

The authors make a distinction between the terms "emotional intelligence" and "emotional literacy." Your IQ score is the result of tests intended to measure your intelligence. Intelligence is defined as "a general capacity of an individual consciously to adjust his/her thinking to new requirements" [Stern, The Psychological Methods of Testing Intelligence, 1914]. To take advantage of your intelligence, you must develop it through learning and practice. One way to do this is to develop your literacy: learn to use language to read and

1

write. In a similar way, we can measure a person's Emotional Quotient or EQ. But just as having a high IQ doesn't necessarily make you successful or well-adjusted, neither does a high EQ. Your emotional intelligence must be developed to be used well. This can be done by becoming Emotionally Literate.

Emotional Literacy is the ability to recognize and name emotions with ease. We have all learned to read and write, and now we can become fluent with our emotions. This helps us understand ourselves, understand others, and understand why humans act as we do. Building emotional literacy starts with (1) listening to our emotions without judgment, (2) reflecting on what they are trying to tell us, and (3) articulating them in our own way. The more we do this, the more fluent we will become. Noticing and using our emotions as guides and supports will become second nature. Over time we may notice that emotions no longer seem odd or embarrassing. We begin to understand emotions as a nonnegotiable part of being human in the same way that sleeping and breathing are. You might say we accept emotions as part of being human and realize they are as important to living a good life as logic and reason.

INTRODUCTION

How to use this workbook

This workbook is organized into 21 steps. They could be taken on 21 consecutive days or they could be spread over a longer period, such as 21 weeks. What we would not recommend is doing more than one step or lesson each day. The reason is that emotional learning requires time and reflection. Things that are not clear to you today may emerge with clarity tomorrow. We invite you to enjoy the process and not rush through it. After all, you've been living with your emotions for decades already; taking a month or two to learn about them probably won't hurt anything.

Each day or step has an exercise for you to complete. There is space given for your reflections, but you may need more. We encourage you to dedicate a journal or notebook to your learning and questions.

In some exercises, you are asked to think of or identify emotions. If you find yourself struggling, you might refer to the Emotions List at the end of the workbook. We have listed 150 of the most common emotions, and reading through them may help you identify the one you are looking for.

Enjoy your exploration and learning. We have no doubt it will be of enormous value in expanding your understanding of yourself and the world around you.

Let's begin!

Day I

WHAT ARE EMOTIONS?

Throughout human existence, emotions have been understood in many ways. The first step in Emotional Literacy is to articulate what emotions are. Do the following exercise and then reflect on the interpretation we offer.

Exercise:

Imagine you are talking with a six-year-old and he or she asks you to explain what an emotion is. What would you tell him or her?

Emotions are ...

_____

_____

_____

The root of the word "emotion" is Latin and means "that which moves us." In other words, emotions are an energy within us and urge us to move or take action in some particular way. Understood this way, emotions are not just about hugging and crying but are a fundamental source of energy that allows us to engage in life. Thinking is an important precursor to action, but the energy that moves the body is emotions. Thinking itself doesn't move us; emotions do.

To conclude today's exercise, see if you can write a definition that satisfies you in your own words:

NOTICING YOUR EMOTIONS

We are never not in an emotion. If we stop and take note, we will find that there is always an emotion present within us. Sometimes there are several, but there is always at least one. A beginning step in emotional literacy development is to learn to notice your emotions.

Exercise:

Reflect on your day since you woke up this morning and write down all the emotions you can recall as best you can.

_____   _____

_____   _____

_____   _____

How many did you write down? Take two more minutes to recall your day and see if there aren't a few more.

_____   _____

_____   _____

_____   _____

What is the total number? Is that surprising?

Highlight and count how many of them you noticed in the moment they were occurring.

Reflect and write on your ability to notice your emotions and the impact that has on your life:

Day 3

NAMING YOUR EMOTIONS

One thing language has the power to do is distinguish between things. This gives us choice. Imagine if you couldn't articulate the difference between an orange and a carrot or between a dog and a cat. You wouldn't be able to explain to other people what you are talking about. The value of this exercise is to help you begin naming emotions in the same way you learned the names of fruits or countries or people in your family. Begin naming them, and over time you will know the name of each without thinking.

Exercise: Reflect on the past hour and write down all the emotions you can recall. Do your best. If you aren't sure what to call one of them, name it as best you can. If you can't name it exactly, write down "something like ..." and put a name.

_____   _____

_____   _____

_____   _____

_____   _____

How many emotions did you list? Were there some you experienced more than once? Go back to the ones you were unsure about and see if you can name them more precisely.

Do you notice any patterns? If so, write them down:

For the remainder of the day bring your attention to naming your emotions as they occur. This won't always be possible, but do your best. The more you practice naming your emotions, the greater your awareness and range will become.

Day 4

FEELINGS AND EMOTIONS

It is not unusual for us to use the words "feeling" and "emotion" interchangeably, but they are different. A "feeling" is the sensation you experience in your body that signals which emotion you are in. We may feel a knot in our stomach or a constricted throat, which is a sign that we are experiencing an emotion. We then interpret that feeling into the emotion. For instance, we may say that the knot in our stomach "means" we are anxious. In this way feelings inform us about the emotions we are experiencing.

Exercise:

Without changing anything, notice the sensations or feelings you are having at this moment. What emotions are they pointing to? It may take a few moments to even notice the feelings, because many times we do not pay attention to them. Do you feel tension somewhere? Do you feel energy moving around your body? Do you feel quiet or restless? Record your feelings and see if you can name a corresponding emotion. Repeat this exercise several times throughout the day.

Feeling

Emotion

11

THOUGHTS AND EMOTIONS

Thoughts and emotions are intimately linked and co-creative. If you think about a time someone cheated you, you'll begin to feel angry. This is because anger is connected to the story of injustice or being treated wrongly. The reverse is also true. If you feel anger and examine your thoughts, you will notice they are related to injustice you've seen or experienced.

Exercise:

Write down the emotions you can name from the past hour. Next to the emotion write what fundamental story is triggering the emotion. Be aware to look for the root story. Your first story will probably be an incident that is personal, but there is also an underlying story that always occurs along with that emotion. An example is that you might feel sad because your dog ran away or a friend moved to another part of the country or a relative passed away. These are the individual stories of sadness. The underlying story that is common to them all is that you have "lost something you cared about." That is the root story of sadness.

Emotion

Root Story

Day 6

IMPULSES AND EMOTIONS

Every emotion moves us in some way. And each emotion has its own unique impulse. For instance, when we experience joy, we "feel like celebrating," and when we experience loyalty, we "feel like defending a person or group important to us." Just because we "feel like" doing a certain thing doesn't necessarily mean we will. That depends on the moment and whether that action is socially appropriate. In some cases, we'll reserve the impulse for later when the circumstances are better suited to express it.

Make a list of emotions you've experienced recently. Next to each emotion write the impulse you felt. Again, it doesn't mean you did that thing, but it is what the emotion made you want to do. Just like with the underlying story of each emotion, look for the underlying impulse. Each emotion has one, and if we understand these, we can predict how we or others will probably behave based on the emotion being experienced.

Emotion	Impulse (what you felt like doing)

Day 7

PURPOSE OF EMOTIONS

Every emotion has a purpose. You might say it "takes care of us" in a certain way. Fear keeps us safe from danger, trust keeps us from taking excessive risk, anger tells us what we believe is just and unjust, etc. Being able to see the purpose of each emotion allows us to respect and value them. Emotions are not random. They are there to help us, guide us, and protect us.

Exercise:

Make a list of emotions you have experienced in the past week. Next to each, write your understanding of the purpose of that emotion and how is it helpful, beneficial, or takes care of you. If you find this challenging, keep the list available, and as an emotion's purpose occurs to you, make a note of it.

Emotion

Purpose

17

REACTING AND RESPONDING

If we put together all you've learned so far, it adds up to the wisdom available to us if we understand emotions. Emotional Literacy is our ability to use emotions in daily life. One important skill to develop is to practice responding rather than automatically reacting. When we put together all the elements and understand our emotions fully, we can choose an effective response.

Think of a strong emotion you have felt recently. Deconstruct it in the following way:

    a.   Name the emotion.

    b.   Identify its underlying story or information.

    c.   What was your impulse or reaction?

    d.   How was that emotion supporting or caring for you?

And the final questions:

    1.   How would you respond to that situation effectively?

    2.   What emotion would allow you to respond effectively?

a. Emotion:

b. Story:

c. Impulse:

d. Purpose:

1. Response you would like to have:

2. Emotion that will produce that response:

EMOTIONS AND MOODS

Although we often use these words interchangeably, they are different. Every emotion has a corollary mood. We can experience resignation as an emotion and live in it as a mood. One difference is the length of the experience. Emotions are quite short, rarely lasting longer than an hour or two. Moods last much longer, and we even live in a mood. You will notice that some people seem to "fall back" to the mood of sadness when not stimulated, while others seem to gravitate to ambition or gratitude. A very important distinction is that emotions are "reactions to an experience or event" and moods "precede and give meaning to an experience or event." In other words, moods are the lens through which we see and understand our experiences.

If one lives in the mood of fear, everything will appear dangerous, but someone who lives in ambition sees a world full of possibilities. Imagine an architect working in the mood of inspiration vs. the mood of resentment. The way in which they apply their technical expertise will depend on their mood because it has an impact on how they see and interpret the world.

Exercise:

In the sections below, first write down the emotions you have experienced in the past week and the event that provoked them. Next write down the moods you've noticed yourself in and how those moods have colored your understanding.

Emotion

Event

Mood

Meaning it produced

Day 10

ASSESSMENTS OF EMOTIONS

Without realizing it, we have learned to think about emotions as either "good" or "bad." If we begin to list the "bad" emotions, we would probably include anger, jealousy, envy, greed, arrogance, and others we would like to avoid. In the "good" category we might list love, generosity, tolerance, and compassion, among others. What this means is that we have prejudgments about emotions. The problem this creates is that we tend to seek out the "good" emotions and avoid the "bad" ones.

Every emotion serves us, but can also get in our way. Fear keeps us safe, but can also immobilize us. Anger tells when we encounter injustice, but sometimes causes us to harm others. Generosity prompts us to share our resources with others, but can also leave us without sufficient means to take care of ourselves.

With the list of emotions below write (1) your assessment of the emotion (good, bad, terrible, indispensable), (2) how it can be helpful, and (3) how it can be a barrier.

- Jealousy

- Fear

- Ambition

- Frustration

- Resentment

- Acceptance

- Love

- Resignation

- Envy

- Greed

- Gratitude

Day 11

EMOTIONS ABOUT EMOTIONS

If we experience shame about our anger or pride in our ambition, we are having emotions about our emotions. We all do, but it can cause us challenges in the emotional domain. What happens is that we get sidetracked by the second emotion, and thus we don't experience the original emotion. Because of that, we lose the information the first is trying to give us about our experiences. The emotion we have about another emotion is often something learned from our family or culture and, in that context, probably served a purpose. Outside of that context it may hinder us from experiencing and understanding our emotions at their most fundamental level.

Exercise:

With each of the emotions below, think of a time you experienced it, and reflect and make note of any emotions that emotion triggered. For example: "I felt lazy but I was embarrassed and so I tried to hide it." Imagine where you might have learned to react to the first emotion with another emotion. Next look for ways your second emotion prevents you from experiencing the first and what you miss by avoiding it.

- Enthusiasm

- Laziness

- Serenity

- Dignity

- Anger

- Frustration

- Lust

- Happiness

- Generosity

- Resentment

- Nostalgia

DRAMA AND EMOTIONS

It isn't unusual for us to confuse drama with emotion. If emotions are the energy that moves us, drama is the level of the energy with which we express it. It is common to talk about Italians being "very emotional," but it is more accurate to say that they are "very dramatic." Culturally, they are known to express their emotions with a high level of energy and animation. Humans all have emotions, but the level of expression is often dictated by culture and individual personality. Simply because we don't see an energetic expression does not mean emotions are not present. Most of us have expressed anger by ignoring or "turning a cold shoulder" on the other person. It is a powerful expression of anger, but is not as dramatic as shouting or throwing things.

Exercise:

Pick a movie or television program to watch. While watching, note below what emotions you observe and what drama or dramatic actions you see. What do you observe about the two and the connection between them?

Now repeat the exercise with a movie from another cultural source. For example, if the first movie was American, pick a French movie for contrast. If the first was Spanish, pick a Danish movie for contrast.

Now watch two videos or movies. Pick ones from different genres. For instance, you might pick a romance and a horror film. What do you observe about the emotions and drama levels in these examples?

TIME ORIENTATION OF EMOTIONS

Many emotions and moods have a strong time orientation. In other words, if you listen to them, they are telling you about past events, current ones, or future possibilities. Regret, nostalgia, and wistfulness are related to the past. Serenity, acceptance, and joy are focused in the present. Fear, ambition, and anticipation are about the future. By noticing the time orientation of the emotions and moods you experience, you can begin to see the orientation of your life. Do you spend more time and attention "living in the past" or "aspiring toward the future"? Often the solution to a strong emotion that pushes you off balance can be shifting to an emotion of a different time orientation. For instance, anxiety tells us something unknown may endanger us in the future. If we put our attention on serving others out of care or compassion, we will find that the anxiety does not have the same energy because we have shifted our time orientation.

List the first 12 emotions that come to mind from your recent past (or refer to the list at the end of the workbook). Next to each one put the time orientation using **past, present, or future**. Count the number in each category. Reflect on what this tells you about the direction of your attention in life.

1.

2.

3.

4.

5.

6.

7.

8.

9.

10.

11.

12.

DIRECTION OF REFERENCE OF EMOTIONS

Just as emotions have a time orientation, many also have a direction of reference. Some are focused inward or on ourselves and others are focused outward on other people. Some refer to groups or organizations. Anxiety and doubt are generally personal concerns, while care, compassion, and generosity are focused on others. Loyalty and shame are emotions associated with groups or organizations, and others like faith and gratitude have to do with the universe or the unknown. Knowing the point of reference of the emotion tells us a lot about our cares and concerns and where we put our attention in life.

Write 12 emotions you often experience at random below. After each emotion describe what you think the point of reference is. Notice any patterns to your list and the most common points of reference.

1.

2.

3.

4.

5.

6.

7.

8.

9.

10.

11.

12.

Day 15

KEY MOODS IN LIFE

There are as many moods as emotions. And like emotions, we experience some more than others. There are four moods that are very common and that have a unique relationship: resentment, resignation, acceptance, and ambition (or enthusiasm). You will see in the model that resentment and resignation occur when we oppose or resist something; resentment when we resist facticities* (those things we believe we cannot change), resignation when we resist possibilities (those things we believe we can change). Acceptance occurs when we accept facticities and ambition when we accept possibilities.

	FACTICITIES	POSSIBILITIES
RESIST	Resentment	Resignation
ACCEPT	Acceptance (or Peace)	Ambition (or Enthusiasm)

See if you can identify a situation in which each of these moods is present for you. You may feel long-standing resentment toward someone in your family or you may repeatedly find yourself feeling ambitious about your work. For each of the four moods find a situation that repeats itself. Once you have done that, write out the "story" you are living in terms of acceptance or resistance of facticities or possibilities. For example, you might remember a story where you tried and tried until you gave up. That is a description of the mood of resignation. Or you might identify a time when you believe something unfair happened to you at work, which describes resentment.

Reflect on your writing and how these four moods are key elements that shape your life:

*Facticities are those things "we believe to be unchangeable," just as possibilities are those things "we believe to be changeable." It is a real word, although not often used.

Day 16

YOUR MOOD IN LIFE

Emotions and moods are areas in which we learn, have knowledge, and gain wisdom. Some part of them is wired into us and an extension of our biology, but the other part is learned. Emotional learning is different from cognitive learning. Cognitively we learn through insight, and it is almost instantaneous. Emotionally we learn through immersion, and it takes much longer. When we experience an emotion repeatedly or live in the mood of a situation, we will begin to absorb it and it will become part of our emotional makeup. This is called limbic revision.

On a separate sheet of paper draw the floor plan of the first house you remember from your childhood. Take your time to place the rooms you remember, and little by little put notes on key elements or events you recall. As you continue, include the exterior—yard, play area, garden, etc.—until you have a full picture. Think about the light, smells, rhythms and sounds you experienced there. Reflect on the mood or moods you most often experienced in this house and surroundings. How is that mood part of your life today? What parallels do you notice? How is the mood you live today the same or different from the mood of that home and time?

Day 17

DECONSTRUCTING EMOTIONS

Taking the learning from days 5, 6, and 8 (Story, Impulse, and Purpose) allows us to deconstruct emotions to understand them linguistically. What that means is that every emotion can be seen to have three elements: (1) It tells a story or it gives us information, (2) it has an impulse or puts us in action in a specific way, and (3) it has a purpose or "takes care of us" in some way. As an example, if we deconstruct the emotion of loyalty, we find that:

1. We feel we are part of a group or relationship (the underlying story)
2. We will try to protect the group or other person (the impulse or reaction)
3. It allows us to protect/take care of the group (purpose)

This deconstruction allows us to understand the key elements that make loyalty the emotion it is. The value of this is first, we have a working understanding of the emotion, its name, its energy, and its purpose. Second, when we hear someone sharing an experience (language), we can know immediately what emotion they experienced, and that allows us to have an idea about their actions. For example, if we hear a co-worker say he/she thinks it was unfair they didn't get a promotion, we will be aware they are in resentment and may try to "get even." Knowing these elements of each emotion makes our own actions more understandable and helps us understand others more deeply.

Go to the list of emotions at the back of the workbook and select four to deconstruct into their three component parts. Articulate them as they make sense to you. Since all emotions are interpretations, you will say it in your own way. As you think about and learn the emotion more deeply, you will find the deconstruction that serves you best.

EMOTION 1:
- o Story:
- o Impulse:
- o Purpose:

EMOTION 2:
- o Story:
- o Impulse:
- o Purpose:

EMOTION 3:
- o Story:
- o Impulse:
- o Purpose:

EMOTION 4:
- o Story:
- o Impulse:
- o Purpose:

Day 18

EMOTIONAL CLUSTERS

Although each emotion has its own identity or profile, there are emotions that are easily confused, either because they feel similar or they often occur together. We call these emotional clusters, and being able to distinguish each individually is an enormous help in understanding what they are telling us and how we want to respond. A few of the most common clusters are:

- Fear, anxiety, and doubt
- Frustration, anger, and indignation
- Service and sacrifice
- Empathy, sympathy, compassion, and pity

For an example of how to clarify which emotion or emotions we are experiencing, let's take a look at fear, anxiety, and doubt. When someone feels anxious, it is often the case that what they are experiencing includes some fear and some doubt. The way we can distinguish the mix is to listen to the story. If they are thinking that something may harm them but they aren't sure what, they are experiencing anxiety. If they are thinking something specific may harm them ("getting hit by a bus"), it is fear. If they are thinking "I'm not sure I know how to get there" or "I am not sure how my audience will receive my presentation," it is doubt. This is important, because unless we know which story is generating the emotion, we cannot adjust it.

Exercise:

Review one of your previous lists of emotions. Ask yourself if you are sure the emotion you wrote is the only emotion you were experiencing. Were there other emotions that were part of your experience? What emotions feel similar to the emotion you wrote down? Deconstruct the emotions and differentiate them either by the sensation you felt, the impulse you were drawn to, or the story you were thinking.

NOT QUITE EMOTIONS

Besides emotions, we have ways of expressing our emotional condition that are not exactly emotions. For instance, when we say we are "burnt out" or "overwhelmed," we are suggesting something is going on emotionally, but several emotions could be the source of those expressions. For instance, we may be overwhelmed with joy, gratitude, fear, anxiety, exhaustion, or despair. Understanding which emotion or emotions are producing the sense of overwhelm can help us navigate them. In some cases, being overwhelmed isn't a bad thing or something we need to address, but in other cases it is important for our health and well-being that we do address it. To do that, we need to know which emotions are provoking the sense of overwhelm.

Make a list of expressions you use or hear that indicate your emotional state but are not precisely emotions. One way to recognize these "emotional indicators" is to ask yourself if more than one emotion can provoke it. If you are unsure about one, check it against the list of emotions at the end of the book. Once you have a list of eight or ten emotional indicators, speculate next to each one which emotions it might be pointing to. For instance, if you put that you feel "heavy," you might be experiencing disappointment or sadness, while feeling "over the moon" could be joy, delight, excitement, or enthusiasm.

EMOTIONAL PALETTE

The aim of emotional literacy is to develop your emotional palette. That means that instead of having a dozen emotions to choose from, you have fifty or a hundred. That knowledge allows you to be more selective and precise in identifying and articulating your emotions. It means you will be more aware of and have more emotions available to you as you move through life. It could be compared to a painter having a full palette of colors to select from.

Go to the list of emotions in the back of the workbook and choose five emotions you want to learn more about below. For each one, answer the following series of questions:

- o   When is a time you can remember experiencing this emotion?
- o   Why do you think it showed up as a result of that experience?
- o   What feelings (sensations) helped you identify this emotion?
- o   What do you think it was trying to tell you or inform you of?
- o   How did it support you?

EMOTION 1:

EMOTION 2:

EMOTION 3:

EMOTION 4:

EMOTION 5:

Day 21

EMOTIONAL LITERACY JOURNEY

For the past 21 days (or lessons) you have been building a new understanding of emotions, ranging from what they are to your personal palette. Any of the exercises can be repeated, and each time you do, it will give you new insights into emotions on both a theoretical level and an experiential one. We encourage you to continue your learning in this way.

There are other possibilities as well. There is an old expression in educational circles that says "learn, do, teach." You have been learning in these weeks, so now is the time to "do" or practice what you have learned and to teach it. The more you do these two, the deeper your understanding will become. In the Resources section at the end of the workbook you'll find ways to connect with the authors for other programs we lead. Some are in person, some virtual. Some are group learning, others are individual. All of them revolve around helping people develop their emotional literacy.

Whatever path you choose, we encourage you to **practice**. Nothing is learned deeply and sustainably without it. Many times, we pick up an idea and learn "about" the thing, but emotional learning requires immersion, and that occurs when you practice. Think of it like learning to play the piano. Your teacher showed you how, the music gave you the path and reminders, but learning to play was something you alone could make happen, and it occurred when you committed to practice on a regular basis.

Exercise:

Reflect and write a short history of your journey. What were the highlights? What was new? What confirmed something you already knew? Think about the emotion in which you are writing and the emotions that are provoked as you write. How would you sum up your experience since you began the workbook? Imagine the story you would tell if it had been an actual journey or vacation trip. Finally, where will you go from here and how will you stay in the exploration of emotions to continue your journey?

CONCLUSION

Thank you for taking this journey into emotional literacy with us. Lucy and I believe humans are at the point in our evolution when understanding emotions and the role they play in all our actions is deeply needed. Our experience over the past 18 years teaching emotional literacy, coaching leaders, and training coaches has shown us the extent to which our emotional education has fallen short. This shouldn't be a surprise given that the focus of formal education is almost entirely intellectual, and in one way we see it as good news. Ignorance can be erased through learning, and we all have a world to learn about emotions and how they make us who we are individually and collectively.

It has been our pleasure to be part of your journey. We wish you the best and hope that our paths cross again, giving us the opportunity to both grow in this area.

A final offer: If you would like to discuss your learning or have Dan or Lucy review your insights and discoveries, please send us a request at dan@dannewby.me. We would be delighted to know what impact these steps had on your emotional literacy and will answer any questions you might have. Looking forward to hearing from you.

Warmly,
Lucy and Dan

ABOUT THE AUTHORS

Lucy Núñez and Dan Newby are coaches, coach trainers, authors, and teachers. They are married and live in Barcelona. Lucy has studied Psychology, Human Relations and Organizational Consulting, Group Dynamics, and several models of coaching. Her professional background includes training coaches for many years, and she has had a long career as a trainer and consultant working with organizations and leaders. She is a native of Venezuela and emigrated to Spain in 2001. Dan is U.S.-born, with 25 years of business leadership experience. For eight years, he was a Senior Course leader for Newfield Network Coaching School in the United States, Canada, and Europe, and now works independently. His clients include for-profit, educational organizations, and NGOs. He leads both in-person and online courses in emotional literacy for coaches and leaders. Both Lucy and Dan are keenly interested in human learning, how it is applied culturally, organizationally, and personally, and, of course, emotions.

RESOURCES/MORE INFORMATION

Please feel free to contact either Lucy or Dan at these email addresses:
Lucy Núñez: lucynunez.alg@gmail.com
Dan Newby: dan@dannewby.me

OUR WORK

Books: Dan and Lucy are co-authors of the book **"The Unopened Gift: A Primer in Emotional Literacy."** It is available in Spanish with the title "Emociones: Un Regalo por Abrir: Introducción a la Alfabetización Emocional." Both are available on Amazon and Kindle.

Workshops: We offer workshops several times a year for coaches who would like to deepen their understanding of emotions and learn ways to use emotions as a tool to increase the effectiveness of their coaching. If this idea interests you, please write to us at dan@dannewby.me.

Coaching: Both Lucy and Dan offer individual coaching. We have experience working with executives and managers at all levels and from many cultural backgrounds. Dan coaches only in English and Lucy in Spanish. Coaching can take place in person or through video conferencing.

Coach Mentoring: We offer mentoring for coaches, whether for certification renewal or to enhance skills. These sessions can be individual or group. They are generally done by video conference, but can be arranged in person. Contact us at dan@dannewby.me.

Facilitation: Both Lucy and Dan have a long history of facilitation for groups, particularly in leadership development and emotions. We offer programs customized to the needs of your team or organization. For more information write to dan@dannewby.me.

Online Training: We offer online training in "Emotions and Coaching" or "Emotions and Leadership" and related themes. These programs are asynchronous and can be accessed from any part of the world. They can be customized or combined with in-person work. More information is available at www.studyemotions.com. For online programs focused on the aviation sector, please visit www.safetyrelations.com.

EMOTIONS REFERENCE LIST

This list, compiled by the authors, includes about 150 of the most common emotions. As you read through it, you may find some you would include in your own list and you may find some you would not classify as emotions. We invite you to decide for yourself. In our research, we have never found a universal, comprehensive list of emotions. Each is different depending on the background and criteria of the list-maker. Our background is coaching, so we are considering these on practical grounds and each had to meet the three criteria of (1) an underlying story, (2) an impulse of predisposition, and (3) a human purpose. Certain emotions in this list can also be classified in other ways. For us, honor can be thought of as an emotion, and it is also a value. Commitment can be an emotion and at the same time, a behavior.

One exercise you might try is placing a check mark next to each of the emotions you use in conversation and thinking. This will tell you which you distinguish linguistically and is a good starting point to gauge your emotional literacy.

- [ ] Acceptance
- [ ] Admiration
- [ ] Adoration
- [ ] Adventurous
- [ ] Affection
- [ ] Aggravation
- [ ] Agony
- [ ] Amazement
- [ ] Ambition
- [ ] Amusement
- [ ] Anger
- [ ] Anguish
- [ ] Annoyance
- [ ] Anticipation
- [ ] Anxiety
- [ ] Apathy
- [ ] Appreciation
- [ ] Apprehension
- [ ] Arrogance
- [ ] Astonishment
- [ ] Attraction
- [ ] Awe
- [ ] Bliss
- [ ] Boldness
- [ ] Boredom
- [ ] Calm
- [ ] Care
- [ ] Certainty
- [ ] Compassion

- [ ] Confidence
- [ ] Confusion
- [ ] Contempt
- [ ] Courage
- [ ] Curiosity
- [ ] Cynicism
- [ ] Delight
- [ ] Denial
- [ ] Desire
- [ ] Despair
- [ ] Dignity
- [ ] Disappointment
- [ ] Disgust
- [ ] Dislike
- [ ] Dismay
- [ ] Dispassion
- [ ] Dissatisfaction
- [ ] Doubt
- [ ] Dread
- [ ] Ease
- [ ] Ecstasy
- [ ] Elation
- [ ] Embarrassment
- [ ] Empathy
- [ ] Enthusiasm
- [ ] Entitlement
- [ ] Envy
- [ ] Equanimity
- [ ] Eroticism

❒ Euphoria	❒ Jealousy
❒ Excitement	❒ Joy
❒ Exhilarated	❒ Kindness
❒ Expectant	❒ Lascivious
❒ Exuberance	❒ Laziness
❒ Fear	❒ Livid
❒ Frustration	❒ Loneliness
❒ Fury	❒ Love
❒ Generosity	❒ Loyalty
❒ Gratitude	❒ Lust
❒ Greed	❒ Magnanimous
❒ Guilt	❒ Melancholy
❒ Happiness	❒ Mischievous
❒ Hate	❒ Misery
❒ Hilarity	❒ Modesty
❒ Honor	❒ Mortified
❒ Hope	❒ Naiveté
❒ Hopelessness	❒ Nostalgia
❒ Horror	❒ Obligation
❒ Hubris	❒ Optimism
❒ Humility	❒ Panic
❒ Impatience	❒ Paranoia
❒ Incredulity	❒ Passion
❒ Indifference	❒ Peace
❒ Indignance	❒ Perseverance
❒ Infatuation	❒ Pessimism
❒ Inspiration	❒ Pity
❒ Intrigued	❒ Pride
❒ Irreverence	❒ Prudence

- ☐ Rage
- ☐ Rebelliousness
- ☐ Regret
- ☐ Remorse
- ☐ Resentment
- ☐ Resignation
- ☐ Respect
- ☐ Reverence
- ☐ Revulsion
- ☐ Righteousness
- ☐ Sadness
- ☐ Satisfaction
- ☐ Scorn
- ☐ Sentimental
- ☐ Serenity
- ☐ Shame
- ☐ Shyness
- ☐ Skepticism
- ☐ Stubborn
- ☐ Surprise
- ☐ Sympathy
- ☐ Tenderness
- ☐ Terror
- ☐ Thankfulness
- ☐ Timidity
- ☐ Tolerance
- ☐ Trust
- ☐ Uncertainty
- ☐ Vengeance
- ☐ Wistfulness
- ☐ Wonder
- ☐ Yearning
- ☐ Zeal